ANIMAZE !

A Collection of Amazing Nature Mazes

by WENDY MADGWICK

illustrated by LORNA HUSSEY

templar publishing

For my grandparents
Dan and Agnes Johnson — L.H.
For my family — W.M.

A TEMPLAR BOOK

First published in the UK in hardback in 1993 by Ragged Bears Ltd.,
This edition published in 2000 by Templar Publishing,
an imprint of The Templar Company plc,
Pippbrook Mill, London Road, Dorking, Surrey, RH4 1JE,
www.templarco.co.uk

Distributed in the UK by Ragged Bears Ltd.,
Ragged Appleshaw, Andover, Hampshire, SP11 9HX

First softback edition

ISBN 1-84011-336-7

Designed by Janie Louise Hunt
Colour separations by Positive Colour Ltd.,
Maldon, Essex, Great Britain

Printed in Hong Kong

Finding the way

A little zebra is lost in the grasslands. He's trying to reach his mother, but cheetahs are lurking nearby, and a hungry lioness is on the prowl.

You can help by finding the right path through the grassland maze and the other nature mazes in this book. Each maze is set in a different habitat — from the icy Arctic to the tropical jungles of South America. Trace the correct path through the maze with your finger. Along the way you'll meet lots of other animals — strange little fish that climb trees and walk on mud, a desert cat that can knock birds out of midair, and more. But be careful — the wrong path could lead to trouble.

All the solutions are at the back of the book, where you'll also find "nature notes" that will tell you about the animals in each picture.

SWAMPLANDS

Silently the evening tide has swept into the mangrove swamps that surround Borneo, an island in South East Asia. Startled, a male proboscis monkey looks up as he hears the call of the other monkeys on the mainland. He has been exploring and is now stranded on a small island. The other monkeys are feeding along the shore and he wants to join in the feast. A strong swimmer, the monkey can weave his way through the water and get back to shore — but some paths are blocked by the tangled roots of the mangrove trees and the creatures that inhabit this strange world. Can you find the way back?

A WORLD IN MINIATURE

In the gloom of a South American jungle, tiny leaf-cutter ants
are cutting off pieces of leaf to take back to their underground
nest. Then they scuttle along the forest floor, following well-worn
scent trails that will lead them home. But they must be careful.
Many of their trails are blocked by other animals. A sticky-tongued
anteater is on the prowl, looking for a meal. Fierce-jawed soldier
termites block another path, and a tiny antbird is pecking its way
along another. Only one route leads home, but which one?
See if you can find the safe path back to the ants' nest.

UPSTREAM

At long last the exhausted salmon have reached their journey's end. They have travelled hundreds of kilometres across the sea to return to the North American river in which they were born. Now they must make their way upstream to the spawning grounds, where the females will lay their eggs. The journey is beset by many hazards — rockfalls block the way, and bears and ospreys fish for their dinner as otters and beavers swim and play in the streams. Follow the maze of waterways and see if you can find the route to the salmon's spawning ground. Only one stream is safe, however. All the rest lead to disaster.

DESERT WASTES

As the afternoon draws to a close and the shadows lengthen,
the animals of the Sahara desert make their way toward the oasis
for a much-needed drink of water and to feed on seeds and
insects. Some animals are already there, lapping up the cool
water. Other animals are on their way. Which animals reach the
oasis safely? Follow the hoofprints of the camel and oryx,
the pawprints of the fox and caracal, and the tiny marks left by
the jerboa and gerbil as they hop across the plain.
Which ones make it safely to the water hole?

THE OUTBACK

The bark of a dingo as it calls to its pups echoes across the plains of the Australian outback. Startled, three little red kangaroos, called joeys, look up. They have become separated from their mothers. Frightened, they rush back to the safety of their mothers' pouches. But the way is not clear, they must avoid many objects. Mallee fowl are nesting, and two young emus scratch at the grassy scrubland near their father. Termite mounds tower over the landscape, and the fearless thorny devil and Gould's goanna scuttle into the shade to escape the heat of the sun. Which joey belongs to which mother? Follow the trails and see if you can find out.

TO THE SEA

In the early morning, just before sunrise, on a lonely beach in Costa Rica, hundreds of newly hatched green turtles scrabble from their underground nests to the surface of the sand. They begin to make their way to the sea. But their journey is not easy. Some are confused by the twinkling lights of a nearby village, mistaking them for the moon glinting on the sea. Others fall prey to raccoons and coatis. Gulls hover overhead, waiting to swoop, and other shore creatures block the way. Some turtles even fall into the deep ruts made by a beach buggy as it churned its way across the wet sand. Can you tell which turtles will make it safely to the sea? Follow their trails and find out.

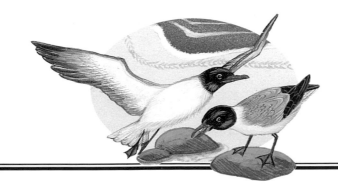

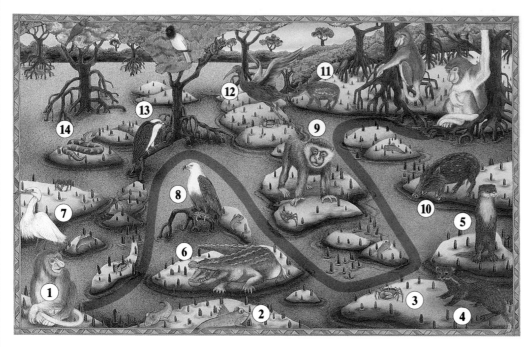

SWAMPLANDS

The mangrove swamps have once again been submerged by the incoming evening tide. A proboscis monkey must swim back to the jungle, but his path is blocked. The tangled roots of the mangrove trees sprout finger-like above the water, while the fearsome crocodile waits, jaws open, ready to pounce! Only one path is safe.

1. Proboscis monkey Proboscis monkeys spend most of their time in the tree tops feeding on leaves, fruit and flowers. The male's long, bulbous nose straightens out when he makes his loud, honking call.

2. Mudskipper These strange little fish can climb, walk and skip over the mud. Their large mobile eyes help them to see well out of water, and they move by using their strong pectoral (shoulder) fins.

3. Fiddler crab The male fiddler crab has one small and one huge claw. Its small claw is used for feeding. Its large claw plays a dual role, used both as a weapon to warn off other males, and to wave invitingly to attract a passing female.

4. Crab-eating mongoose This mongoose hunts alone, usually at night, feeding on crabs and similar creatures. The mongoose marks the boundary of its den with a scent to warn away other animals.

5. Eurasian otter Now rare, Eurasian otters live in burrows, called holts, in the river bank. Good swimmers, they use their large, webbed hind feet and thick, muscular tails to propel them through the water. Their nostrils and ears can be closed when they are swimming.

6. Salt-water crocodile One of the largest and most dangerous of animals, the estuarine crocodile is hunted for its skin and is now protected in many areas. Able to live even in salt water, it rarely comes on land.

7. Great egret Like all herons, the egret hunts in water. It waits motionless until it sights its prey, which it then seizes in its strong, sharp beak.

8. Sea eagle Sometimes called fishing eagles, these large birds have rough surfaces on the underside of their toes to help them grasp their slippery prey.

9. Crab-eating macaque Mostly active during the day, these small, long-tailed monkeys live on the ground near water. They feed on crabs and other small animals.

10. Bearded pig These large pigs have white whiskers on their cheeks and large warts beneath their eyes. They feed on plants and fruit, often following groups of monkeys and picking up the food they drop.

11. Lesser mouse deer The smallest of the mouse deer or chevrotains, weighing only 2 kg, these shy creatures mainly come out at night. They do not have horns or antlers, but the males have long upper canine teeth that hang down below their jaws.

12. Glossy ibis The most widespread ibis, it feeds on insects and water creatures. The female nests in a tree or reed bed, and both parents care for the eggs and young.

13. Osprey At breeding time, the osprey, or fish hawk, builds a large nest on the ground from sticks and seaweed. The same nest is often used year after year until it becomes huge. The male feeds the female while she incubates the eggs and he also helps to feed the fledglings.

14. Mangrove snake A great many of these rear-fanged snakes live at the swamp's edge, feeding on crabs and fish.

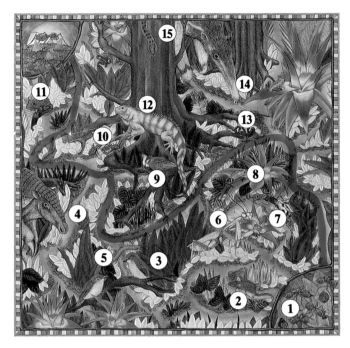

A WORLD IN MINIATURE

In the dense South American jungle, tiny leaf-cutter ants march back to their nests. But their way is blocked by many hazards, from hungry birds to the sticky-tongued anteater. Only one path leads safely to the nest.

1. Leaf-cutter ant These tiny jungle insects cut off pieces of leaf with their sharp jaws and take them back to their nest. They carry the pieces, often larger than themselves, over their heads like enormous umbrellas. Because of this, they are also called parasol ants.

2. Spiny pocket mouse These tiny, bristly mice, sometimes called rice rats, usually come out at night to feed on seeds.

3. Ochre-bellied flycatcher This active little bird flits from tree to tree seizing insects and spiders in its hook-tipped bill.

4. Giant armadillo The largest armadillo, weighing up to 60 kg, this animal has an armoured body with movable horny plates.

It feeds on ants and termites, smashing their hills with its large-clawed front feet and flicking them up with its tongue.

5. Tropical centipede These fast-moving creatures have a pair of poison claws (modified front legs) just behind their head. This tropical species can grow up to 30 centimetres long.

6. Praying mantis Motionless, mantises sit hidden among the greenery, with their legs held as if in prayer, waiting to pounce on their unsuspecting prey.

7. Long-horned beetle The antennae of these beetles can be four times as long as their bodies. The grubs burrow into wood, weakening and spoiling it for building use.

8. Arrow poison frog The brilliant colours of these tiny ground-dwelling frogs warn their enemies that they are poisonous. Local tribespeople extract the poison and use it on the tips of their arrows and blow-pipe darts.

9. Antbird These tiny birds, most of them less than 10 centimetres long, have strong, hooked beaks. Many live on the dense forest floor in Central and South America, feeding on ants and other insects.

10. Soldier termite Termites differ from ants in that when the young hatch, they look like small adults, not grubs. The powerful jaws of some soldier termites can snap an ant in half.

11. Horned frog As broad as it is long, this large-mouthed frog spends much of its life half-buried in the ground.

12. Common iguana These agile tree-living lizards feed on plants, but they can defend themselves with sharp teeth and claws if attacked by predators.

13. Caecilian These strange limbless creatures look like giant earthworms but are in fact amphibians. Caecilians burrow into the soft soil of the forest floor in search of their prey of earthworms and insects and rarely appear above ground.

14. Giant anteater A giant anteater, walking on the knuckles of its front feet to protect its sharp claws, snuffles over the forest floor in search of food. Like the armadillo, it demolishes ant nests and termite mounds, then mops up the insects with its sticky tongue, which can extend up to 60 centimetres.

15. Anaconda One of the largest snakes at up to 12 metres long, the anaconda can climb small trees and shrubs but never strays far from water.

PATHWAYS IN THE SNOW

As the summer sun warms the frozen Arctic tundra, the snow melts and for a brief time flowers bloom and animal life abounds. As daylight fades, the female lemmings and their pups must return to their burrow. But only one path leads to home.

1. Caribou These North American reindeer travel over 1,000 km twice a year between their summer and winter feeding grounds. Their habit of digging through the snow to find food led the Micmac Indians to call them *caribou*, meaning "shoveler".

2. Arctic wolf Fierce hunters, a pack of Arctic wolves may travel over 1,000 km as they hunt caribou. Their ghostly howls keep them in touch with one another and warn other packs to keep away.

3. Pomarine skua These summer visitors breed on the tundra, feeding on lemmings. Skuas lay up to three brown eggs, which hatch into mottled honey-brown chicks.

4. Ringed seal In the winter, when ice covers the seas, ringed seals use the long sharp claws on their front flippers to cut holes in the ice. After diving to hunt fish, the seals surface at these holes to breathe.

5. Snowy owl Daytime hunters, snowy owls feed on Arctic hares and lemmings. They nest in May in small hollows lined with moss and feathers. The male feeds the female while she incubates the eggs.

6. Musk ox Their long, shaggy coats and dense underfur keep musk ox warm in the freezing Arctic winter. When threatened, they form a tight circle, with their heads and horns pointing at the enemy.

7. Arctic fox In its smoky grey summer coat, the Arctic fox blends in with its background. Its short ears and muzzle and furry-soled feet help to keep it warm in the freezing snow, and its snow-white winter coat conceals it from its enemies and its prey.

8. Canada goose When Canada geese migrate to their breeding and summer feeding grounds, these large birds always follow the same route and often breed in the same area where they were born.

9. Arctic hare Easy to recognize with their long, black-tipped ears and long hind legs, Arctic hares usually live alone. They rest in small burrows in the ground or in shallow depressions called forms. In the winter they grow a white coat.

10. Polar bear Excellent swimmers with "webbed" toes, polar bears spend most of their lives hunting seals among the ice floes. In summer, they journey across the land, feeding on lemmings and plants.

11. Trumpeter swan These beautiful birds breed on the tundra, laying their eggs in a nest of grass and moss lined with swan's down. When the cygnets are less than 90 days old, trumpeter swans journey south to overwinter in a warmer climate.

12. Walrus The walrus uses its snout and tusks (long canine teeth) to pry shellfish from the ocean floor. The food is then gathered into the mouth by the mobile lips.

13. Lemming These little animals are active even in winter, feeding on the seeds and plants they find in their snow tunnels. Lemmings usually have two litters a year. At times the number of animals increases so enormously that they have to find new places to live. They often swim across lakes and rivers and may even try to swim the sea.

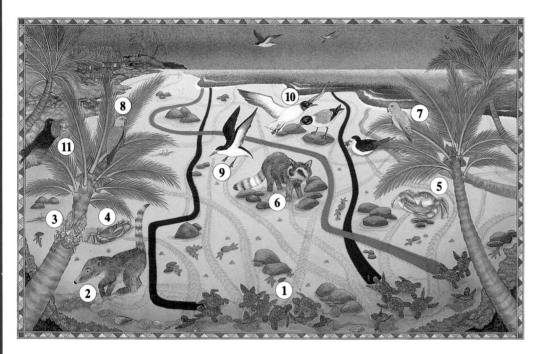

TO THE SEA

As the newly hatched green turtles make their way to the sea, they are confronted by many dangers — raccoons, coatis and gulls, which will eat them, and the twinkling lights of a nearby town, which confuse them. Only a few of the hatchlings will reach the safety of the sea.

1. Green turtle At nesting time, green turtles travel hundreds of kilometres to lay their eggs on the beaches where they were born. The female makes a hollow in the sand with her front flippers. Lying in this hollow, so that her shell is level with the sand, she digs a deep hole with her hind flippers and lays over 100 eggs. She covers the nest with sand and returns to the sea. The eggs hatch 2 to 3 months later. The hatchlings dig their way out and head for the sea. Many die. The green turtle is now an endangered species because it has been hunted for its eggs, hide and meat, and is losing its habitat along the beach.

2. Coati Although they usually live in woods and lowland forests, coatis will venture on to beaches to hunt for food.

The coati snuffles in the ground with its long, mobile snout, feeding on insects, spiders and small animals. It will also dig up and eat turtle eggs as well as the young hatchlings.

3. Robber crab The robber crab weighs up to 2 kg and is half a metre long. It climbs trees, feeding on fruit and coconuts.

4. Land crab Square-bodied land crabs feed on both plants and animals. They live mainly on land, only occasionally returning to the sea.

5. Ghost crab This sand crab lies in burrows beneath the sand with just its long eye stalks visible. The ghost crab usually feeds on sand flies but also attacks newly

hatched turtles, catching them by a flipper and dragging them underground.

6. Raccoon The raccoon hunts at night, using its front paws and long fingers to handle its food. It climbs well and can also swim. Although it usually lives in woods and swamps near water, it will also forage on beaches, digging up turtle eggs and hunting for hatchlings.

7. Spectacled parrotlet Found throughout Central America, these small parrots live in noisy, chattering flocks of between 5 and 20 birds. They live in open forest, feeding on berries, buds, blossoms and fruit.

8. Yellow-headed parrot Good talkers, these bright, colourful parrots are under threat because they are collected in large numbers for the cage-bird trade. They are also in danger from the destruction of their forest homes.

9. Black skimmer Skimmers have a special way of catching fish. They fly just above the surface of the sea so that their flattened lower bill cuts through the water. When a skimmer comes upon a fish or crab, it snaps its upper bill closed, pulls it head sharply back to swallow its prey, and keeps on flying. In spring, when skimmers breed, the female scrapes out a hollow in the sand in which she lays 2 to 4 eggs.

10. Black-headed gull These small, active gulls feed on almost anything. Their black heads are part of their breeding plumage. Colonies of gulls nest on marshes and coasts in the spring.

11. Magnificent frigate bird This beautiful bird catches its prey of fish, crabs and, on this occasion, baby turtles by swooping down on them. The male has a large, red throat pouch which he blows up like a football to attract females.